Grade 5

The Syllabus of Examinations should be read for details of requirements, especially those for scales, aural tests and sight-reading. Attention should be paid to the Special Notices on the front inside cover, where warning is given of changes.

The syllabus is obtainable from music dealers or from The Associated Board of the Royal Schools of Music, 14 Bedford Square, London WC1B 3JG (please send a stamped addressed C5 envelope).

In overseas centres, information may be obtained from the Local Representative or Resident Secretary.

Requirements

SCALES AND ARPEGGIOS (from memory)

Scales

(i) in similar motion, hands together one octave apart, and each hand separately, in *all* major and minor keys (melodic *or* harmonic minor at candidate's choice) (all three octaves)

(ii) in contrary motion, both hands beginning and ending on the key-note (unison), in the keys specified in one of the following groups chosen by the candidate:
Group 1: A, F, D♭ majors and harmonic minors
Group 2: D, F♯, B♭ majors and harmonic minors
(two octaves)

Chromatic Scales

(i) in similar motion, hands together one octave apart, and each hand separately, beginning on any note named by the examiner (three octaves)

(ii) in contrary motion, both hands beginning and ending on the same note (unison), beginning on D and A♭ (two octaves)

Arpeggios

the major and minor common chords of *all* keys, in root position only, in similar motion, hands together one octave apart, and each hand separately (two octaves)

PLAYING AT SIGHT (see current syllabus)

AURAL TESTS (see current syllabus)

THREE PIECES

Candidates must prepare Nos. 1 & 2 from the *same* list, A *or* B, but may choose No. 3 from *either* list *or* one of the further alternatives listed below:

Wolf   Schlummerlied (Lullaby)
Kabalevsky   Song of the Cavalry, Op. 27 No. 29
These are included in A Romantic Sketchbook for Piano, Book III, *published by the Associated Board*

Editor for the Associated Board: **Richard Jones**

© 1997 by The Associated Board of the Royal Schools of Music

No part of this publication may be copied or reproduced in any form or by any means without the prior permission of the publishers.

Music origination by Barnes Music Engraving Ltd. Printed in Great Britain by Headley Brothers Ltd, The Invicta Press, Ashford, Kent and London.

Where appropriate, pieces have been checked with original source material and edited as necessary for instructional purposes. Fingering, phrasing, pedalling, metronome marks and the editorial realization of ornaments (where given) are for guidance but are not comprehensive or obligatory.

A:1

Allemande

First movement from Suite in G minor, HWV 452

HANDEL

Source: autographs, Cambridge, Fitzwilliam Museum, 30.H.11–13.
This Allemande is drawn from one of the two suites that Handel wrote around 1739 for his young pupil Princess Louisa (b. 1724), daughter of King George II. Upbeat quavers should be detached and the lines of left-hand quavers lightly articulated. Semiquavers may be slurred in pairs or detached on occasion for contrast. Dynamics and tempo indications are editorial suggestions only.

Selected from Handel, *Selected Keyboard Works*, Book III, edited by Richard Jones (Associated Board)

poco rall.

Sonatina in F

G. BENDA

Source: *Sammlung vermischter Clavier- und Gesangstücke* (Gotha and Leipzig, 1780–7).
Georg Benda (1722–95) belonged to a large Bohemian family of musicians. He was a violinist in the Prussian court orchestra in the 1740s and later became Capellmeister at the court of Gotha. Dynamics and crossed slurs are editorial suggestions only.

Miniature in D minor

No. 2 from *10 Miniatures en forme d'Études*, Op. 8

GEDIKE

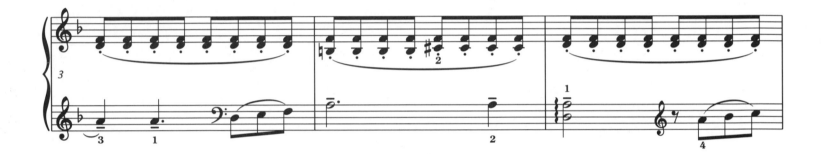

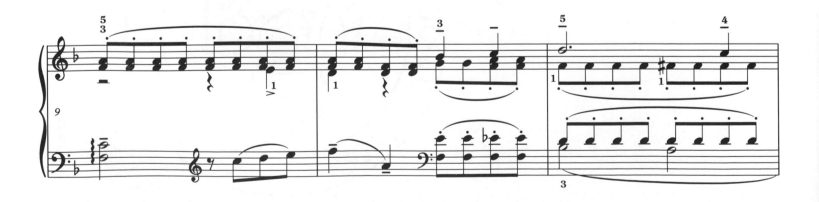

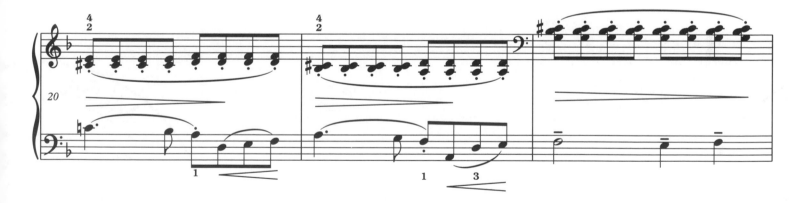

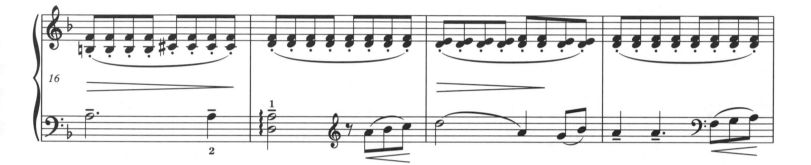

rallentando al fine

B:1

Allegro

First movement from Fantasia No. 10 in A minor

TELEMANN

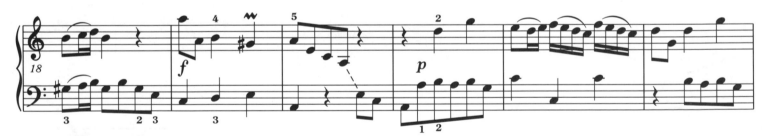

Selected from Telemann, *Fantasias*, First Dozen, edited by Richard Jones (Associated Board)

Source: *Fantaisies pour le Clavessin*, TWV 33 (Hamburg, 1732/3).
Telemann's Fantasias, like Bach's Clavierübung II of 1735, place the French and Italian styles of the day side-by-side in order to illustrate their differences. The first dozen fantasias, from which the A minor is drawn, are written in the Italian style. Quavers should be detached. Ornaments, slurs and dynamics are editorial suggestions only.

B:2

Allegro non tanto

First movement from Sonatina in G, Op. 19 No. 1

Edited by
Lionel Salter

J. L. DUSSEK

Source: *Six sonatines pour le forte piano*, Op. 19 (London, *c*.1792).
Jan Ladislav Dussek (1760–1812) was a Bohemian composer who studied under C. P. E. Bach in Hamburg, toured as a piano virtuoso and performed alongside Haydn in London. Phrasing and dynamics have been supplemented by the editor.

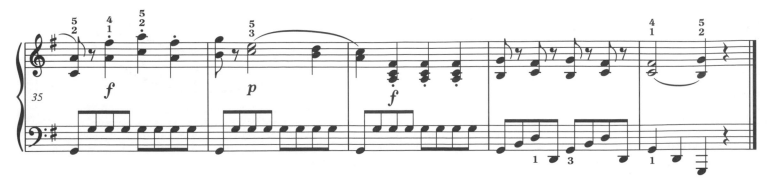

B:3

Blues

Second movement from Sonatine No. 7

GERARD HENGEVELD

Blues tempo [♩ = *c.*116]

Reprinted by permission, for use only in connection with the examinations of the Royal Schools of Music. Sonatine No. 7 is published by Broekmans & Van Poppel, Van Baerlestraat 92–94, Amsterdam, to which all enquiries for this piece apart from the examinations should be addressed.

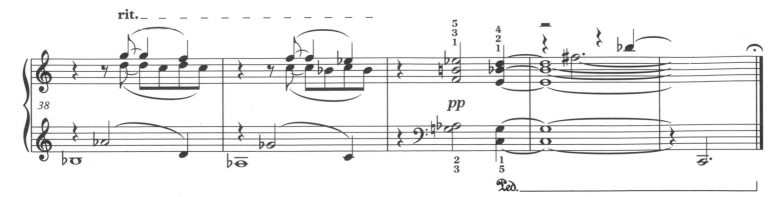